My
Chick Activity
book

p

Add up these animals
and write the answers
in the boxes.

Which path leads to the piglet's dinner?

Join the dots and color in
to discover the farmer's vehicle.

Color this farmyard scene.

Color by numbers.
1=dark green 2=pink 3=black
4=gray 5=yellow 6=light green

Count the cows, sheep, and pigs in this farm scene. Write the numbers in the boxes.

Look carefully at these
two pictures.
Can you find five differences?

Draw lines to match the
mothers to their babies.

9

Draw a line to match each
word with its picture.

tractor

egg

wheat

duckling

goat

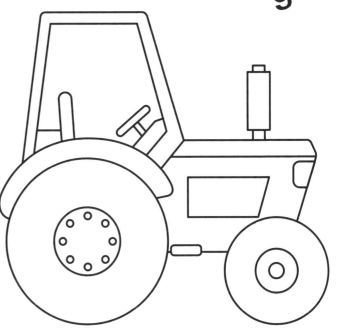

farmer

Join the dots and color in to complete this picture.

Color this noisy rooster.

12

Help the farmer find his
way to his dog in
this field full of sheep.

Draw lines to match the
farmer and his animals
to their homes.

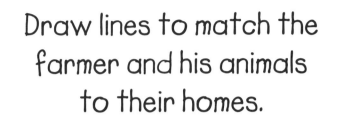

14

Copy the picture of the
fluffy chick into the empty
grid, then color him in.

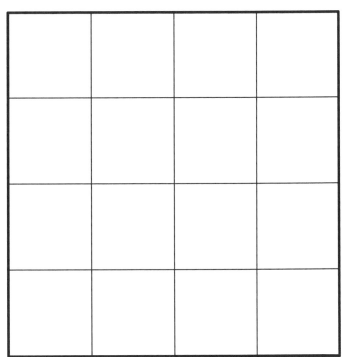

Look at these six pictures
of woolly sheep.
Which one is different?

Color in this busy farm
pond picture.

Join the dots and color in
to see who is about to
eat the flowers.

19

Look carefully at these
two pictures.
Can you find five differences?

21

Draw a line to join each
animal to its shadow.

Color in this picture of
a horse in its stable.

How many cows and calves
can you see?
Write the number in the box.

24

Color in this picture of a farmer and his family picking apples.

25

Help the rooster find his way through this maze to reach his dinner.

Color in this picture of
a donkey in a field.

27

Join the dots to discover
what the tractor is pulling.

Follow the lines to join each animal to its food.

Color in this picture of a fluffy chick, mother hen, and rooster.

30

Draw a line to match each
word with its picture.

sheep

chicken

dog

goat

donkey

31

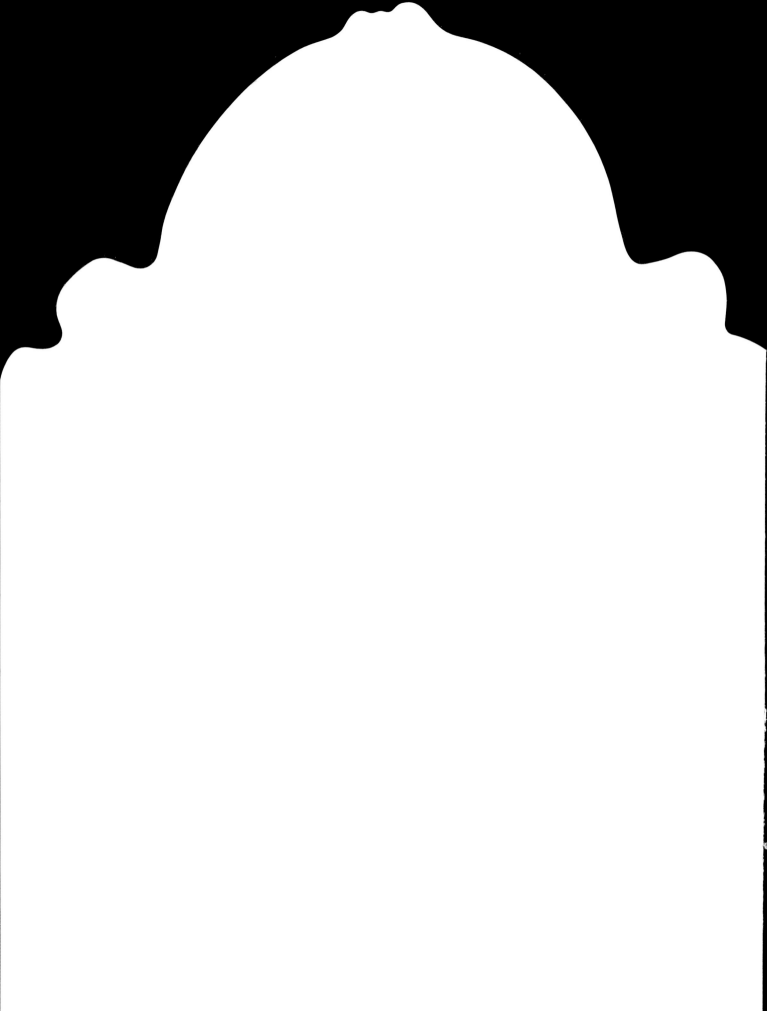

How many animals are there
in each field?
Write the numbers in the boxes.

Color in this picture of
cute bunnies playing in a field.

34

Look carefully at these
two pictures.
Can you find five differences?

Follow the path from each child to find out which animal belongs to them.

Join the dots and color in to complete the busy beehive.

17

16
15   14

20   18
19

12   13
11   10   7
9   8

21   1
6   3   2
5   4

37

Color in this picture of
chicks hatching from their eggs.

Can you find the names of
these animals in the grid below?

cow

duck

pig

t	b	e	s	r	o	h
l	d	o	g	k	s	n
c	o	w	b	j	t	f
u	n	p	e	e	h	s
v	k	c	i	h	c	w
d	e	m	f	g	r	p
k	y	l	k	c	u	d

dog

chick

donkey

sheep

horse

Which two butterflies are the same? Circle them.

This chick has lost his *mommy!*
Help him through the maze
to find her.

Color in this picture of
these farmyard animals.

43

Count the sheep, donkeys, and horses in this picture.
Write the numbers in the boxes.

44

Circle all the things you would use on a farm. Which is the odd one out?

Look carefully at these
two pictures.
Can you find five differences?

Which path leads to
the piglet's mommy?

47

Color in this picture of a farm pond.

Copy the picture of a piglet
into the spare grid, then
color him in.

Four naughty little kittens
are hiding. Can you find them?

52

Color in this picture of naughty little rabbits eating all the carrots.

Draw a line to match each calf to one with the same pattern.

Which tractor has been in which muddy field? Draw a line to match them.

55

Join the dots to complete
this picture.

Look carefully at these
two pictures.
Can you find five differences?

57

Help these children through the maze so they can feed the carrots to the horse.

59

Join the dots to complete this picture.

Answers

Page 2

Page 3

Page 7

Page 8

Page 9

Page 10

Page 13

Page 14

Page 17

Page 21

Answers

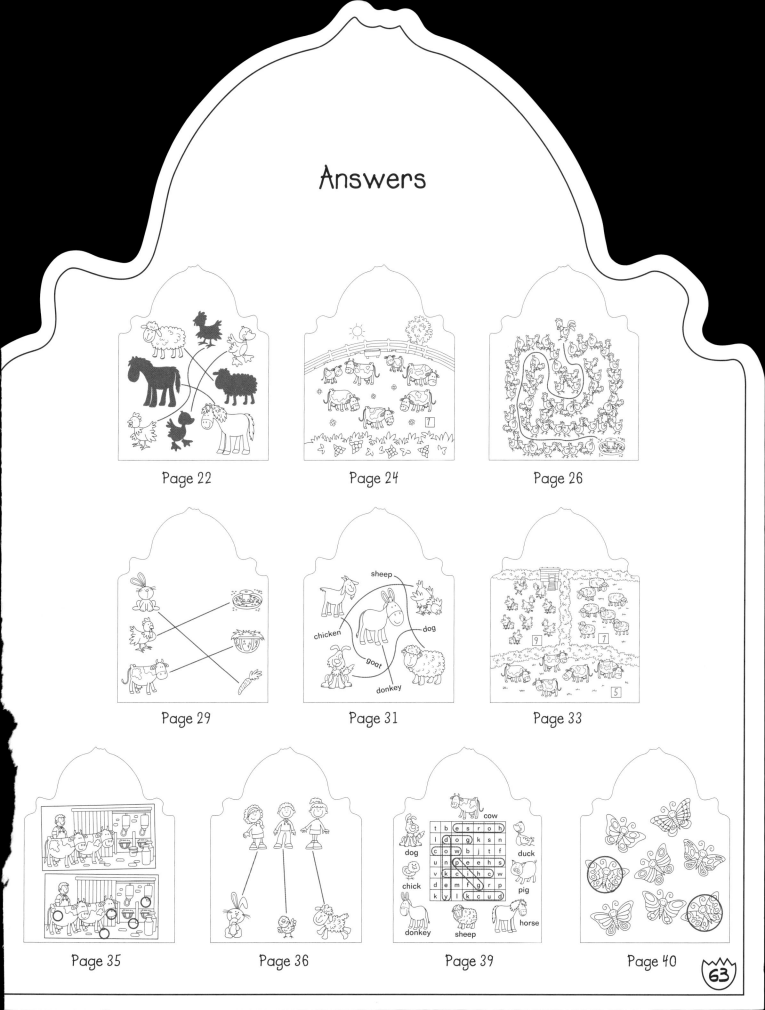

Page 22

Page 24

Page 26

Page 29

Page 31

Page 33

Page 35

Page 36

Page 39

Page 40

63

Answers

Page 41

Page 44

Page 45

Page 46

Page 47

Page 52

Page 54

Page 55

Page 57

Page 59